IT'S ALL ABOUT YOU

First published by Parragon Books Ltd in 2012
LIFE CANVAS is an imprint of Parragon Books Ltd

Parragon
Chartist House
15-17 Trim Street
Bath BA1 1HA, UK
www.parragon.com

LIFE CANVAS and the accompanying logo are trademarks of
Parragon Books Ltd

Illustration p68–71 © iStockphoto/Pingebat

Written by Melissa Heckscher
Edited by Sharyn Rosart
Designed by Lynne Yeamans

ISBN 978-1-78186-133-2
GTIN 5060292801117

Printed in China

IT'S ALL ABOUT YOU

A record of the journey from "me and you" to "us."

MELISSA HECKSCHER

Contents

INTRODUCTION

The following pages are the story of you and me, and how we became us. This book is for recording all the wonderful, romantic, crazy, and fleeting moments that make you, **YOU** and us, **US**.

Because if we don't write it down, we might forget something. And I want to remember it all.

Love, _____

HOW TO USE THIS BOOK

Do it together or do it separately, like this:

[ ] THINK ABOUT YOUR RELATIONSHIP.

[ ] TAKE A DEEP BREATH.

[ ] THEN ANOTHER.

[ ] QUIT PAWING EACH OTHER.

[ ] START WRITING.

[ ] BE HONEST (BUT NEVER HURTFUL).

Who Are You?

The basics of you (as known to me):

Your full name:

Your nicknames:

Your gender:

Your birthday:

Your age right now:

Your age when I met you:

Height:

Weight:

Eye color:

Hair color:

Religion:

Astrological sign:

WHAT I LIKE ABOUT YOU

How I rate you (*on a scale of 1 to 10*):

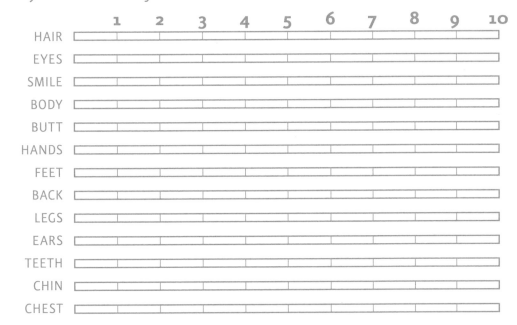

	1	2	3	4	5	6	7	8	9	10
HAIR										
EYES										
SMILE										
BODY										
BUTT										
HANDS										
FEET										
BACK										
LEGS										
EARS										
TEETH										
CHIN										
CHEST										

My favorite part of you is

Your Look

My favorite items in your closet:

1
2
3
4
5

My least favorite of your clothing:

Your favorites:

1
2
3

Your Personality

You are (check all that apply):

[ ] ADVENTUROUS   [ ] CRITICAL   [ ] INTENSE   [ ] PERSISTENT

[ ] AMBITIOUS   [ ] DEPRESSED   [ ] INTROVERTED   [ ] PRUDENT

[ ] ANGRY   [ ] DOWN-TO-EARTH   [ ] JEALOUS   [ ] REPRESSED

[ ] ANXIOUS   [ ] DREAMY   [ ] KIND   [ ] RISK-TAKING

[ ] ARGUMENTATIVE   [ ] EASYGOING   [ ] LAID-BACK   [ ] ROMANTIC

[ ] ARTSY   [ ] ENERGETIC   [ ] LAZY   [ ] SAD

[ ] ASSERTIVE   [ ] FAMILY-ORIENTED   [ ] LONELY   [ ] SATISFIED

[ ] BORING   [ ] FRUGAL   [ ] LOVING   [ ] SENSITIVE

[ ] BRAVE   [ ] FUNNY   [ ] LOYAL   [ ] SHY

[ ] CAREER-ORIENTED   [ ] GENEROUS   [ ] MYSTERIOUS   [ ] SMART

[ ] COLD   [ ] HAPPY   [ ] NERDY   [ ] TALKATIVE

[ ] COMPETITIVE   [ ] HUMBLE   [ ] NERVOUS   [ ] UNDERSTANDING

[ ] CONFIDENT   [ ] IDEALISTIC   [ ] NURTURING   [ ] WIMPY

[ ] CONFUSED   [ ] INDEPENDENT   [ ] OUTGOING   [ ] WISE

[ ] CRAZY   [ ] INSANE   [ ] PASSIONATE   [ ] WITTY

[ ] CREATIVE   [ ] INSECURE   [ ] PEACEFUL   [ ] YOUTHFUL

Your Values

Overall, you are (*circle one*): CONSERVATIVE / LIBERAL / PRAGMATIC

What's most important to you:

	VERY IMPORTANT	SOMEWHAT IMPORTANT	DON'T CARE		VERY IMPORTANT	SOMEWHAT IMPORTANT	DON'T CARE
accomplishment				compassion			
achievement				competition			
adventure				creativity			
affection				dependability			
altruism				ecological awareness			
art				excitement			
being the best				empathy			
change and variety				fame			
cheerfulness				family			
cleanliness				financial gain			
community				freedom			

	VERY IMPORTANT	SOMEWHAT IMPORTANT	DON'T CARE		VERY IMPORTANT	SOMEWHAT IMPORTANT	DON'T CARE
friendships				pleasure			
frugality				power and authority			
helping other people				privacy			
honor				recognition			
inner peace				religion			
integrity				resilience			
intellectual status				security and stability			
knowledge				self-respect			
loyalty				sex			
marriage				sophistication			
meaningful work				thoughtfulness			
nature				tranquillity			
nonconformity				truthfulness			
persistence				youthfulness			
physical challenge				wisdom			

10 Words
I USE TO DESCRIBE YOU

1.

2.

3.

4.

5.

6.

7.

8.

9.

10.

What I've Learned About Your Childhood

Where you grew up:

Your parents:

Your siblings:

Your room:

Your pet(s):

A favorite memory:

A childhood accident:

Your best childhood friend(s):

Your first kiss:

5 Things

I LOVE ABOUT YOU

3 Things
I DON'T LOVE ABOUT YOU

Your Favorites

Movie:

Band:

Song:

Book:

Magazine:

Website:

Video game:

Color:

Restaurant:

Bar:

Store:

Food:

Drink:

Subject in school:

Sport to play:

Sport to watch:

Sports team:

Place to relax:

Place to get frisky:

Weekend activity:

Exclamation/thing to say:

Nickname for me:

My Crystal Ball
(WHAT I SEE IN YOUR FUTURE)

=== **You'll be** *(check all that apply)*: ===

[ ] FATTER   [ ] THINNER   [ ] BALDER

[ ] BETTER-LOOKING   [ ] HEALTHIER   [ ] EXACTLY THE SAME

[ ] OTHER _____

=== **You'll live** *(check all that apply)*: ===

[ ] IN A MANSION   [ ] IN A COUNTRY HOME   [ ] IN AN APARTMENT

[ ] WITH YOUR PARENTS   [ ] IN A TRAILER PARK   [ ] ON A SAILBOAT

[ ] OTHER _____

You'll be a *(check all that apply):*

[ ] PROFESSIONAL   [ ] ENTREPRENEUR   [ ] EXECUTIVE

[ ] STAY-AT-HOME PARENT   [ ] ARTIST   [ ] HERMIT

[ ] OTHER _____

You'll be *(check all that apply):*

[ ] WITH ME   [ ] WITH SOMEONE ELSE   [ ] ALL ALONE

[ ] DIVORCED ONCE   [ ] DIVORCED MULTIPLE TIMES   [ ] CELIBATE

[ ] WITH SOMEONE HALF YOUR AGE   [ ] OTHER _____

And you'll *(check all that apply):*

[ ] MAKE MILLIONS   [ ] MAKE PEOPLE HAPPY   [ ] SAVE THE WORLD

[ ] STRUGGLE   [ ] OTHER _____

How We Met

I was here:

_____

_____

You were there:

_____

_____

The **reason** we met was:

_____

_____

_____

_____

Right away *(check one):*

[ ] I KNEW YOU WERE THE ONE   [ ] I WASN'T SURE YET   [ ] WE DIDN'T GET ALONG

MY FIRST IMPRESSION OF YOU

When I first saw you, **I thought**:

_____

_____

When you first saw me, **you thought**:

_____

_____

I was (check one):

[ ] SPOT-ON WITH MY INITIAL FEELINGS   [ ] TOTALLY WRONG ABOUT YOU

You were (check one):

[ ] SPOT-ON WITH YOUR INITIAL FEELINGS   [ ] TOTALLY WRONG ABOUT ME

The first thing that **attracted** me to you was:

Check one:

[ ] I STILL FIND THAT ATTRACTIVE   [ ] I NO LONGER LIKE THAT ABOUT YOU

OUR FIRST CONVERSATION

THE FIRST THING YOU SAID TO ME:

WHAT I SAID BACK:

Our First Date

Where we went:

What we did:

My rating (check one):
[ ] PERFECT   [ ] PRETTY GOOD   [ ] NOT AS GOOD AS THE SECOND ONE

The most **memorable** thing about our first date:

Why I wanted to go out with you **again**:

Going Out

Our **top** 3 early dating moments:

Our **worst** 3 early dating moments:

Our Firsts

FIRST kiss
When:

Where:

Initiated by: ME / YOU / MUTUAL

It was a little: CLUMSY / PERFECT / NOT AS GOOD AS THE SECOND ONE

FIRST fight
When:

Where:

Started by: ME / YOU / MUTUAL

We made up: RIGHT AWAY / AFTER A WHILE / STILL MAD

FIRST "I love you"
When:

Where:

Said first by: ME / YOU

I was a little: NERVOUS / THRILLED / SHOCKED

FIRST TIME WE HAD **sex**

When:

Where:

Initiated by: ME / YOU / MUTUAL

It was: RUSHED / AWKWARD / AWESOME

FIRST **sleepover**

When:

Where:

We had breakfast: TOGETHER / SEPARATELY

We slept: IN EACH OTHER'S ARMS / ON OPPOSITE SIDES

FIRST MAJOR **holiday** WE SPENT TOGETHER

When:

Where:

High point:

Low point:

FIRST **vacation** WE TOOK TOGETHER

When:

Where:

High point:

Low point:

3 Things
THAT DREW ME TO YOU

These things that you did were really **attractive**:

1

2

3

3 Things
I WOULD CHANGE ABOUT YOU

These things I find rather **unattractive**:

1
2
3

Getting Serious

I was **nervous** about getting serious with you because:

_____

_____

_____

_____

How I **overcame** these doubts:

_____

_____

_____

_____

I **wanted** to get serious with you because:

Ò_Ó

WHEN WE KNEW WE

I knew we were a couple when:

_____

_____

_____

You knew we were a couple when:

_____

_____

_____

The first person I told about "us" was:

_____

The first person you told about "us" was:

_____

WERE A COUPLE

What **changed** after we got serious:

_____

_____

_____

Terms of **endearment** we started using once we were a couple:

_____

_____

_____

If we had a couple **nickname** (like "Brangelina") it would be:

_____

_____

The **anniversaries** we celebrate are:

_____

_____

OUR ROMANCE STYLE

As a couple, we are *(check all that apply)*:

[ ] AFFECTIONATE (PRIVATELY)

[ ] AFFECTIONATE (PUBLICLY)

[ ] ADVENTUROUS

[ ] ANGRY

[ ] CHALLENGING

[ ] CODEPENDENT

[ ] COMFORTABLE

[ ] COMMITTED

[ ] CONFLICTED

[ ] COZY

[ ] DRAMATIC

[ ] EDGY

[ ] ENERGETIC

[ ] ENTHUSIASTIC

[ ] FUNNY

[ ] FAITHFUL

[ ] HOMEBODIES

[ ] HARMONIOUS

[ ] HOSTILE

[ ] INDEPENDENT

[ ] INTENSE

[ ] INTIMATE

[ ] JEALOUS

[ ] LAZY

[ ] NURTURING

[ ] OPPOSITES

[ ] PASSIONATE

[ ] PLAYFUL

[ ] PREDICTABLE

[ ] SATISFYING

[ ] SELFLESS

[ ] SILLY

[ ] SURPRISING

[ ] TALKATIVE

[ ] TRADITIONAL

[ ] UNFAITHFUL

[ ] WISE-CRACKING

Our First Fight

Our first **serious** argument was about:

════════════════════ *Circle one:* ════════════════════

[ ] I WAS WRONG [ ] YOU WERE WRONG [ ] WE WERE BOTH WRONG

How we **resolved** it:

═══════ **Since then, we have fought** *(circle one):* ═══════

[ ] NEVER [ ] RARELY [ ] OFTEN

all about **you**...37

We're In Love

It's official, we've said **"I love you"**:

The first time was (*check one*):

[ ] AWKWARD   [ ] EASY   [ ] PASSIONATE   [ ] SPONTANEOUS

After the first time, we said it (*check one*):

[ ] FREQUENTLY   [ ] RARELY   [ ] HAVEN'T SAID IT AGAIN

Who says it more often? (*check one*):

[ ] YOU   [ ] ME   [ ] WE BOTH SAY IT WITH THE SAME FREQUENCY

We say it *(check all that apply):*

[ ] OVER THE PHONE   [ ] IN PUBLIC   [ ] BEFORE BED   [ ] ALL THE TIME

I wish we said it *(check one):*

[ ] MORE OFTEN   [ ] LESS OFTEN   [ ] THE SAME

In public, we *(check all that apply):*

[ ] WALK ARM IN ARM   [ ] HOLD HANDS   [ ] KISS   [ ] NO PDA

Your Place...

Your **place** (*draw or describe here*):

Stuff of yours that I hate:

...or Mine?

My **place** (*draw or describe here*):

Stuff of mine that you hate:

Good Habits

Yours:

[ ] I'M GLAD YOU HAVE THIS HABIT.   [ ] ACTUALLY, IT'S KIND OF ANNOYING.

Mine:

[ ] YOU'RE GLAD I HAVE THIS HABIT.   [ ] ACTUALLY, IT'S KIND OF ANNOYING.

Bad Habits

Yours:

───────────── *Check one:* ─────────────

[ ] YOU SHOULD CHANGE THESE.   [ ] IT'S WHO YOU ARE.

Mine:

───────────── *Check one:* ─────────────

[ ] I SHOULD CHANGE THESE.   [ ] IT'S WHO I AM.

Your Finest Qualities

The 3 qualities of yours that I **value** the most are:

1

2

3

On a scale of 1 to 10, this is how I would rate your:

	1	2	3	4	5	6	7	8	9	10
ATHLETICISM										
COMMITMENT TO OUR RELATIONSHIP										
COMMUNICATION SKILLS										
COOKING										
HONESTY										
INTEGRITY										
INTELLIGENCE										
KINDNESS										
OPENNESS TO NEW SITUATIONS										
OVERALL LOOKS										
POTENTIAL										
PROWESS IN BED										
SENSE OF HUMOR										
SEX APPEAL										
SINCERITY										
WILLINGNESS TO CHANGE										

Your Likes

Your **favorite** things:

kids

nature

shopping

sex

family

eating

holidays

sleeping

rain

work

hanging out

sports

reading

walking

chess

watching tv

traveling

cooking

beer-drinking

gardening

CHART KEY:

_____ [solid]		_____ [dotted]	
_____ [striped]		_____ [light-toned]	
_____ [white]		_____ [mid-toned]	

Your Dislikes

Your **least favorite** things:

kids
nature
shopping
hanging out
sex
sports
reading
family
walking
eating
chess
holidays
watching tv
traveling
sleeping
cooking
rain
beer-drinking
work
gardening

CHART KEY:

_____ [solid]	_____ [dotted]
_____ [striped]	_____ [light-toned]
_____ [white]	_____ [mid-toned]

Seeing Eye to Eye

Some opinions we **agree** on are:

1
2
3
4
5

When these subjects come up, we *(check one)*:

[ ] REINFORCE EACH OTHER'S THINKING   [ ] TRY TO GET OTHERS TO AGREE WITH US

[ ] DON'T NEED TO DISCUSS THEM

Some opinions we **don't agree** on are:

1
2
3
4
5

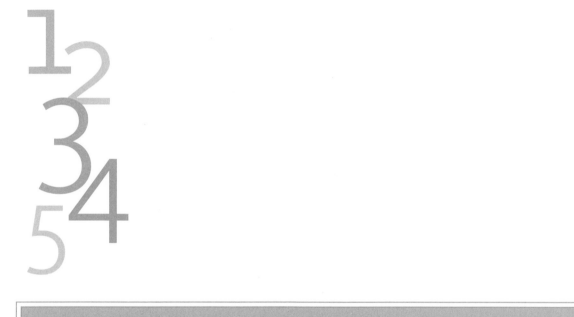

When these subjects come up, we *(check one)*:

[ ] ARGUE   [ ] AGREE TO DISAGREE   [ ] NEVER DISCUSS THEM

Things We Have

We share these **qualities**:

1
2
3
4
5

The shared quality that is most **important** to the happiness of our relationship:

in Common

We do not share these **qualities**:

1
2
3
4
5

The quality we don't share that is most **dangerous** to our relationship:

Our Desert Island

If you were stuck on a desert island,
I think **you would take** these things:

What I was right about:

What I was wrong about:

Necessities

If I was on that island with you,
I'd take these things:

1
2
3
4
5

Why I would take these things:

_____

_____

_____

Your Family Tree

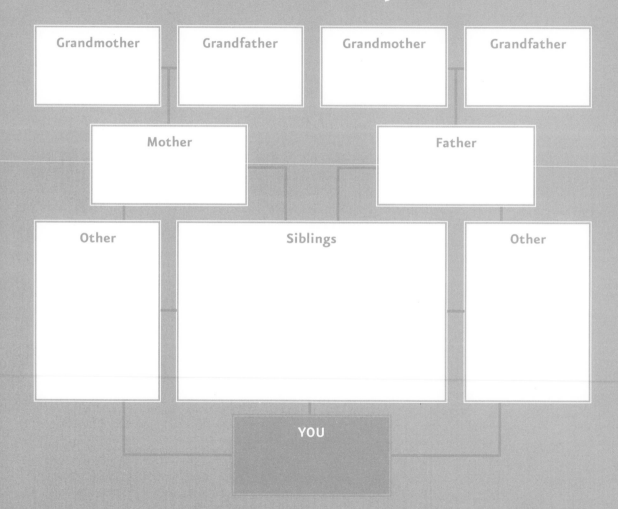

Grandmother	Grandfather	Grandmother	Grandfather

Mother	Father

Other	Siblings	Other

YOU

My Family Tree

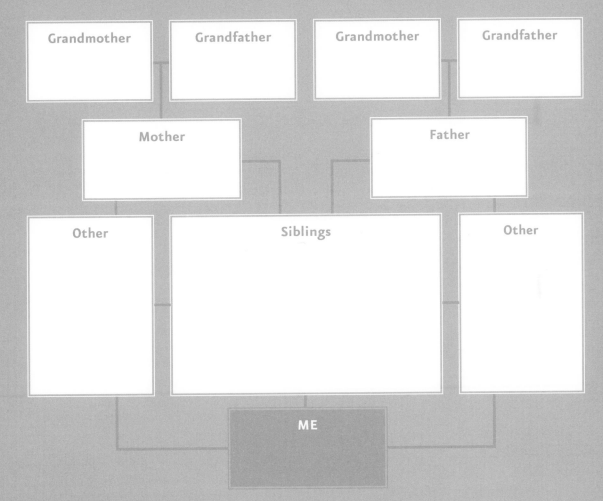

YOUR FAMILY MEMBERS

I've **met**:

_____

_____

_____

I **get along** best with:

_____

I am **intimidated** by:

_____

What they thought of me when I met them:

_____

_____

What they think of me now:

_____

_____

_____

MY FAMILY MEMBERS

You've **met**:

You **get along** best with:

You are **intimidated** by:

What they thought of you when they first met you:

What they think of you now:

Our Friends

Map out our friends here, with circles to designate
the **mutual** friends we share.

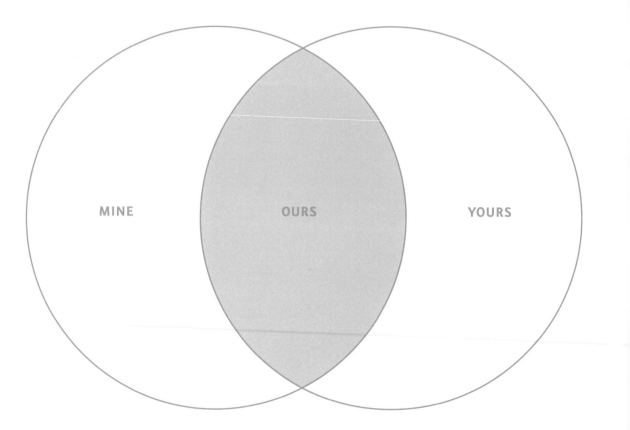

MINE

OURS

YOURS

What We Do Together

Here are the main things we do when we **are** together:

1.
2.
3.
4.
5.

The main things we do when we're **not** together:

YOU:

1.
2.
3.

ME:

1.
2.
3.

Us...at Work

YOUR JOB:

I think your job is:

I WOULD / WOULDN'T trade places with you for a week.

I've met your boss: Y / N
    Liked each other: Y / N

MY JOB:

You think my job is:

You WOULD / WOULDN'T trade places with me for a week.

You've met my boss: Y / N
    Liked each other: Y / N

Our Diversions

My top hobbies and interests include:

1
2
3

Your top hobbies and interests include:

1
2
3

Together, we (check one):

[ ] HAVE NO COMMON INTERESTS   [ ] LIKE TO DO THESE THINGS TOGETHER:

_____

Our Favorite Places

Dinner spot:

Bar:

Coffee joint:

Breakfast place:

Walking route:

Diner:

Romantic dinner place:

Room in the house:

Bookstore:

Movie theater:

Live music venue:

Sports arena:

Friend's place:

Vacation spot:

City:

Small town:

Weekend getaway:

Hotel:

Beach:

View:

Place to enjoy nature:

Place to watch the sunset:

Place to share a kiss:

Place to settle down:

Other:

Other:

Time Together

This is what we do when we are together:

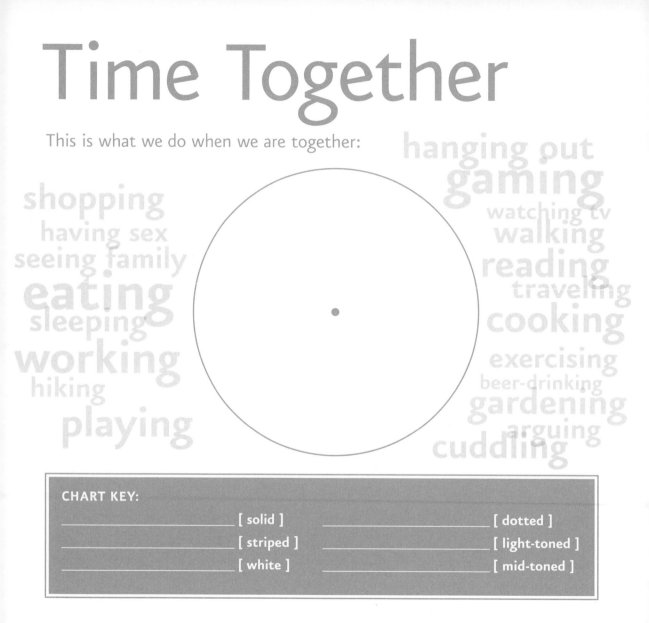

hanging out
gaming
watching tv
walking
reading
traveling
cooking
exercising
beer-drinking
gardening
arguing
cuddling

shopping
having sex
seeing family
eating
sleeping
working
hiking
playing

CHART KEY:

_____ [solid]   _____ [dotted]

_____ [striped]   _____ [light-toned]

_____ [white]   _____ [mid-toned]

OUR BEST TIMES TOGETHER

Most romantic moment:

Best shared meal:

Tastiest meal we made:

Most enjoyable weekend:

Greatest trip:

Sexiest experience:

Most special quiet moment:

Best thing we accomplished together:

Other awesome things we've done together:

A WEEK IN THE LIFE OF US

This is a **typical week** in our relationship:

Monday:

Tuesday:

Wednesday:

Thursday:

Friday:

Saturday:

Sunday:

We **eat** (circle one): TOGETHER / APART
We **sleep** (circle one): TOGETHER / APART
We do this **together:** _____
_____
We do this **separately:** _____
_____

THE PLACES WE'VE TRAVELED TOGETHER

PLACES WE WANT
TO VISIT TOGETHER

WHO'S BETTER AT?

	1	2	3	4	5	6	7	8	9	10	
DANCING											ME
											YOU
COOKING											ME
											YOU
SEDUCTION											ME
											YOU
COMMUNICATION											ME
											YOU
WORKING											ME
											YOU
SPORTS											ME
											YOU
HOME REPAIRS											ME
											YOU
SLEEPING											ME
											YOU
ARGUING											ME
											YOU
SOCIALIZING											ME
											YOU
MAKING PLANS											ME
											YOU

	1	2	3	4	5	6	7	8	9	10	
CLEANING											ME
											YOU
DECORATING											ME
											YOU
SHOPPING											ME
											YOU
FASHION SENSE											ME
											YOU
TALKING TO STRANGERS											ME
											YOU
CONFLICT											ME
											YOU
FINANCES											ME
											YOU
DREAMING											ME
											YOU
HEALTHY EATING											ME
											YOU
FAMILY OBLIGATIONS											ME
											YOU
EYESIGHT											ME
											YOU
PHYSICAL COORDINATION											ME
											YOU

Our Funniest

Something that we both found **hilarious**:

Our favorite **funny** people (FRIENDS, PERFORMERS, WRITERS):

A time I laughed **with** you:

:-D

Moments

:-D

A time I laughed **at** you:

_____

_____

_____

A time you laughed **with** me:

_____

_____

A time you laughed **at** me:

_____

_____

I **still** laugh when I think about:

_____

_____

_____

Turn-ONS

Our **top** 3 turn-ons:

1
2
3

Something that especially turns you on is:

Check one: [ ] I'M INTO THIS   [ ] I'M NOT INTO THIS

Something that especially turns me on is:

Check one: [ ] YOU'RE INTO THIS   [ ] YOU'RE NOT INTO THIS

Turn-OFFS

Your turn-offs:

My turn-offs:

1
2
3

Some things we'd **never** do:

Where We've

The **first** time:

Weirdest spot:

Most **romantic** spot:

Grossest spot:

Done It

Most **public** place:

Most **exciting** place:

Your favorite place to do it:

My favorite place to do it:

Romance Ratings

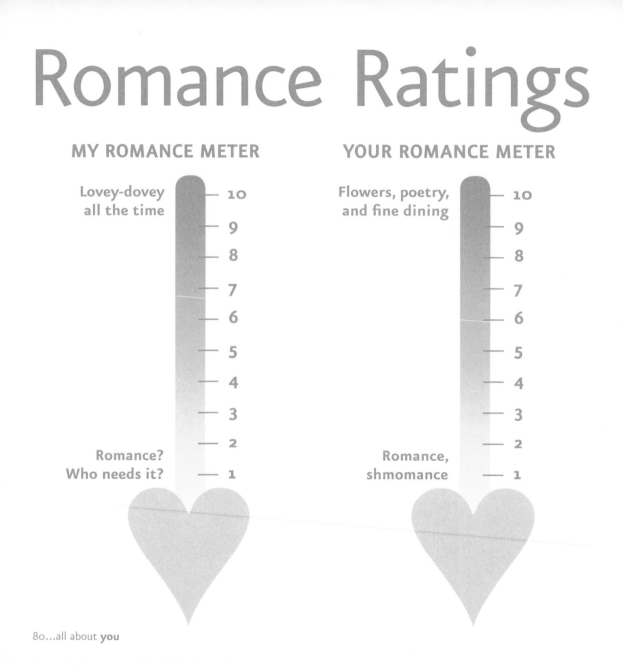

MY ROMANCE METER

Lovey-dovey all the time

Romance? Who needs it?

10
9
8
7
6
5
4
3
2
1

YOUR ROMANCE METER

Flowers, poetry, and fine dining

Romance, shmomance

10
9
8
7
6
5
4
3
2
1

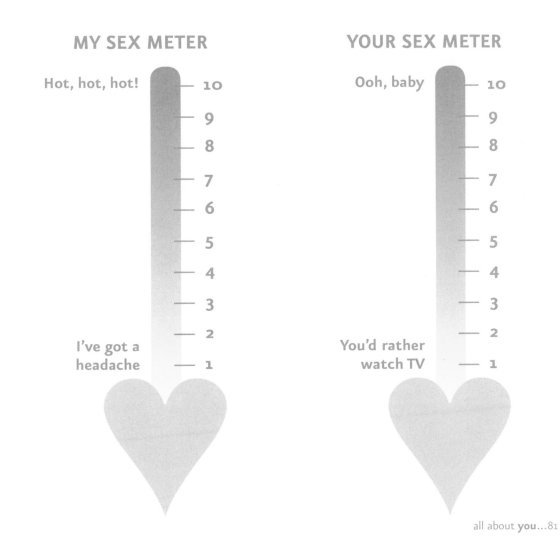

MY SEX METER

Hot, hot, hot! — 10

— 9

— 8

— 7

— 6

— 5

— 4

— 3

— 2

I've got a
headache — 1

YOUR SEX METER

Ooh, baby — 10

— 9

— 8

— 7

— 6

— 5

— 4

— 3

— 2

You'd rather
watch TV — 1

Our Areas of Discontent

These are the areas of our relationship that we fight about—the size of the pie slice corresponds to the intensity of the conflict it causes.

Make your own pie chart:

CHART KEY:
Money [*solid*]
Sex [*striped*]
Work [*white*]
Domestic duties [*dotted*]
Free time [*light-toned*]
Jealousy [*mid-toned*]
Other _____ [*dark*]

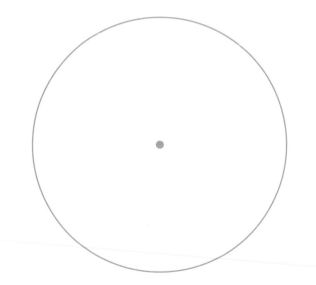

Sweetpea Honeybunch

Some of my nicknames for you:

NICKNAME	HOW IT STARTED	DO YOU LIKE IT?
		YES / NO
		YES / NO
		YES / NO
		YES / NO

Some of your nicknames for me:

NICKNAME	HOW IT STARTED	DO I LIKE IT?
		YES / NO
		YES / NO
		YES / NO
		YES / NO

Our Tunes

A song that reminds me of you is:

A song that describes us best is:

A song you love:

A song I love:

A song we both love:

Your favorite band:

My favorite band:

Our favorite band:

Bands we've seen live:

Bands we want to see live:

Our favorite bedroom music:

Our favorite party music:

The Big (and Little) Screen

The first movie we saw together:

The most recent movie we've seen together:

A movie that reminds me of us:

The movie based on our relationship would be called:

Our favorite movie:

A TV show we like to watch together:

A TV show you won't watch with me:

A TV show I won't watch with you:

Preferred Words

A book that means something to both of us is:

A book that we'll never read together is:

What you're reading now:

What I'm reading now:

We read the same things (*circle one*): all the time/often/rarely/never

A book I wish you would read:

A book you wish I would read:

A website we like:

A magazine we like:

Anecdotal Evidence

A **joke** or **story** you tell that I love is:

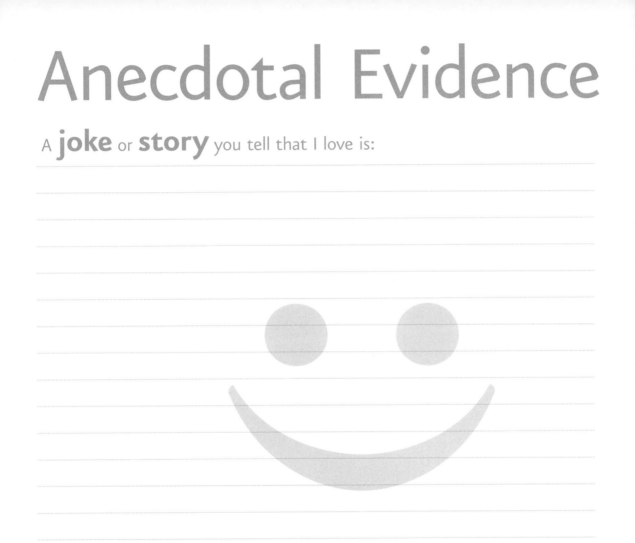

MY FAVORITE PICTURE OF YOU

MY FAVORITE PICTURE OF US

Loving You Has

[ ] A BETTER PERSON	[ ] CRY	[ ] HONEST
[ ] ANXIOUS	[ ] DANGEROUS	[ ] HOPEFUL
[ ] BRAVER	[ ] DISCREET	[ ] HUMBLE
[ ] BUSIER	[ ] DULL	[ ] IMPATIENT
[ ] CODEPENDENT	[ ] FATTER	[ ] INDEPENDENT
[ ] CONFIDENT	[ ] FITTER	[ ] INSECURE
[ ] COOLER	[ ] GLAMOROUS	[ ] INTELLECTUAL
[ ] CRAFTY	[ ] GRATEFUL	[ ] JEALOUS
[ ] CRUEL	[ ] GULLIBLE	[ ] LAZY

Made Me...

[ ] LONELIER   [ ] IMAGINATIVE   [ ] SADDER

[ ] LOYAL   [ ] MORE PASSIONATE   [ ] SEXIER

[ ] MORE AMBITIOUS   [ ] NOISIER   [ ] SMARTER

[ ] MORE ATTRACTIVE   [ ] OBNOXIOUS   [ ] THINNER

[ ] MORE CARING   [ ] POPULAR   [ ] TIDIER

[ ] MORE CRITICAL   [ ] MORE UNDERSTANDING   [ ] TIRED

[ ] MORE DECISIVE   [ ] POORER   [ ] WEALTHY

[ ] GENEROUS   [ ] PROUD   [ ] WIMPIER

[ ] HOSPITABLE   [ ] RELIABLE   [ ] WISE

Since We've Been

I've stopped:

I've started:

I'm more:

I'm less:

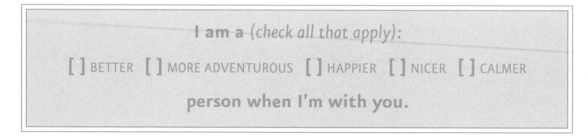

I am a *(check all that apply):*

[ ] BETTER [ ] MORE ADVENTUROUS [ ] HAPPIER [ ] NICER [ ] CALMER

person when I'm with you.

Together...

You've stopped:

You've started:

You're more:

You're less:

You are a (*check all that apply*):

[ ] BETTER [ ] MORE ADVENTUROUS [ ] HAPPIER [ ] NICER [ ] CALMER

person when I'm with you.

Your Reputation

I've heard these **compliments** about you:

1
2
3

I've heard some **less complimentary** things:

1
2
3

Couples We Admire

Real-life couples whose relationship we admire:

_____

_____

_____

_____

Fictional couples we like:

_____

_____

_____

_____

What we've learned from these couples that we would like to do
in our relationship:

_____

_____

_____

_____

On Our Most Memorable Night, We...

[ ] WE WANT TO DO THIS AGAIN   [ ] ONCE WAS ENOUGH

Our Anniversaries

The day we met:

Our first date:

Other important events we like to celebrate:

[ ] YOU ALWAYS REMEMBER THESE THINGS   [ ] I HAVE TO REMIND YOU

So Sorry!

Something I am sorry for:

My excuse was:

Why I think I'll never do it again:

Why I may do it again:

Something you wish I was sorry about:

Something you are sorry for:

Your excuse was:

Why you think you'll never do it again:

Why you may do it again:

Something I wish you were sorry for:

We Are Working

Things that you do that get on my nerves *(check all that apply):*

[ ] SPEND TOO MUCH **/** TOO LITTLE MONEY

[ ] HANG OUT WITH YOUR FRIENDS TOO MUCH **/** NOT ENOUGH

[ ] STILL SEE YOUR EX   [ ] SEND QUESTIONABLE TEXT MESSAGES

[ ] DO TOO MUCH OVERTIME   [ ] LEAVE THE TOILET SEAT UP **/** DOWN

[ ] MAKE A MESS   [ ] HOG THE REMOTE   [ ] DO THE SAME OLD THING IN BED

Things that I do that get on your nerves *(check all that apply):*

[ ] SPEND TOO MUCH **/** TOO LITTLE MONEY

[ ] HANG OUT WITH MY FRIENDS TOO MUCH **/** NOT ENOUGH

[ ] STILL SEE MY EX   [ ] SEND QUESTIONABLE TEXT MESSAGES

[ ] DO TOO MUCH OVERTIME   [ ] LEAVE THE TOILET SEAT UP **/** DOWN

[ ] MAKE A MESS   [ ] HOG THE REMOTE   [ ] DO THE SAME OLD THING IN BED

On...

Your fighting style is mainly *(check one):*

[ ] AGGRESSIVE   [ ] PASSIVE-AGGRESSIVE   [ ] SILENT TREATMENT

[ ] OTHER _____

How we resolve our fights *(check one):*

[ ] I GIVE IN   [ ] YOU GIVE IN   [ ] WE COMPROMISE   [ ] WE HAVE SEX

We go to bed angry *(check one):*

[ ] NEVER   [ ] SOMETIMES   [ ] REGULARLY

Romance Coupons

FROM _____ TO _____

This coupon is good for one romantic evening with 3 activities of your choice:

1. _____

2. _____

3. _____

This coupon expires on: _____

FROM _____ TO _____

This coupon is good for one sexual act of your choosing:*

_____

This coupon expires on: _____

*THE SMALL PRINT: Excludes: _____

FROM _____ TO _____

This coupon is good for one sensual massage.

This coupon expires on: _____

FROM _____ TO _____

This coupon is good for a movie night with **your** choice of movie.

This coupon expires on: _____

FROM _____ TO _____

This coupon is good for the realization of one fantasy:*

Fantasy requested: _____

This coupon expires on: _____

*THE SMALL PRINT: Excludes: _____

My Apologies

Dear _____,

I'm sorry because...

_____
_____
_____
_____
_____
_____
_____
_____
_____

Check all that apply.

[ ] I'LL NEVER DO IT AGAIN.

[ ] I'LL TRY NOT TO DO IT AGAIN.

[ ] I MAY DO IT AGAIN. SORRY.   *Photocopy and use as needed.*

Dear _____ ,

Please forgive me for...

_____
_____
_____
_____
_____
_____
_____
_____
_____
_____
_____
_____

Check all that apply.

[ ] I SHOULDN'T HAVE DONE THIS.

[ ] I SHOULDN'T HAVE TOLD YOU THAT I DID THIS.

[ ] I'M SORRY YOU SAW ME DOING THIS.   *Photocopy and use as needed.*

Fill-in-the-Blank

Date: _____

Dear _____ ,

In the _____ (circle one) YEARS / MONTHS

we've been together, not a day goes by when I don't think

to myself, " _____ !
                        (exclamation)

I'm so lucky to have you in my _____ ."
                                           (noun)

Not only are you _____ ,
                              (adjective)

Photocopy and use as needed.

Love Letter

but you're also _____ ,
(adjective)

_____ ,
(adjective)

and _____ .
(adjective)

I (circle one) LOVE / LIKE YOU so much. Thank you for making me the
(choose one) HAPPIEST / LUCKIEST / COOLEST / RICHEST / MOST NEUROTIC

person in the world. You're the _____ !
(adjective)

(circle one) LOVE / KISSES / HUGS / SINCERELY,

_____

Photocopy and use as needed.

Our Future
THINGS WE'D LIKE TO DO TOGETHER

This month:

1.

2.

3.

4.

5.

This year:

1.

2.

3.

4.

5.

In the next five years:

1.

2.

3.

4.

5.

Someday:

1.

2.

3.

4.

5.

Our Goals

Your life goals:

1.

2.

3.

My life goals:

1.

2.

3.

Our shared goals:

1.

2.

3.

I Promise...

YOU PROMISE...A LETTER FROM ME TO YOU

To be opened on _____ (insert date, one year from today)